BLUES BROTHER SOUL SISTER

PIANO/VOCAL/GUITAR

Folio © 1993 International Music Publications Limited
Southend Road, Woodford Green, Essex IG8 8HN

Printed by Panda Press · Haverhill · Suffolk

Cover Artwork supplied by Dino Entertainment Ltd.

215-2-957

BLUES BROTHER

SOUL SISTER

BOOM BOOM

Words and Music by
JOHN LEE HOOKER

Boom boom boom boom, gon-na shoot you right down

wear off___ a' your feet,

take you home with me, put you in my house___

boom boom boom boom.

(2.) Ow how how

(Talk)

I like it like that.

On ᛏ. to Fade

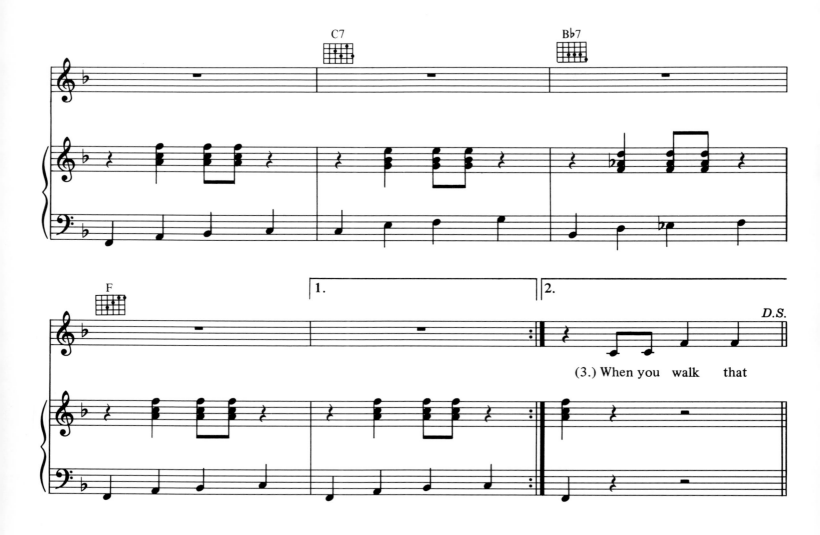

(3.) When you walk that

VERSE 2:
Ow how how how
Mm mm mm mm
Mm mm mm mm
I love to see you strut
Up and down the floor
When you're talking to me
That baby talk.

VERSE 3:
When you walk that walk
And talk that talk
And whisper in my ear
Tell me that you love me
I love that talk
When you talk like that
You knock me out
Right off my feet.

DRIFT AWAY

Moderate

Words and Music by
MENTOR WILLIAMS

GREEN ONIONS

Music by
BOOKER T. JONES, STEVE CROPPER,
AL JACKSON Jr. and LEWIE STEINBERG

Solo

HARLEM SHUFFLE

Words and Music by
BOB RELF and EARL NELSON

18

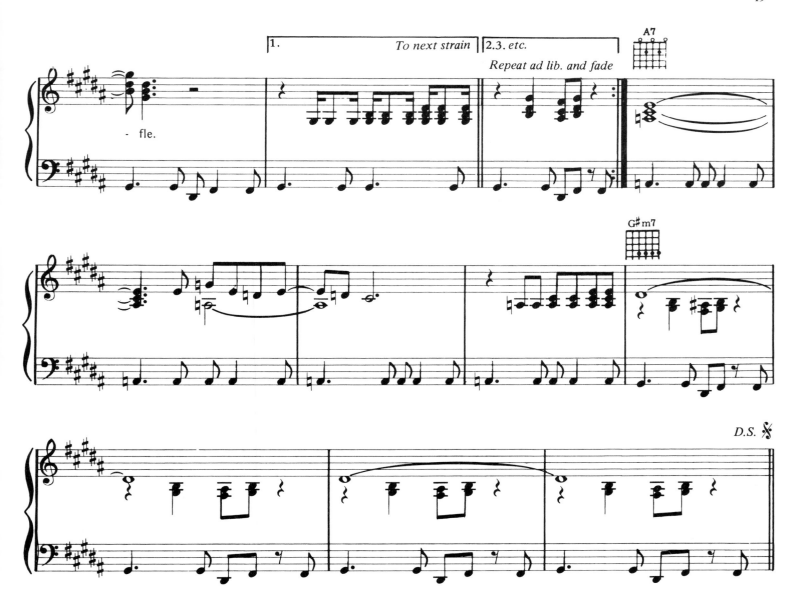

Verse 2:
You scratch just like a monkey, yeah, you do - real cool.
You slide it to the limbo - yeah. How low can you go?

Now come on, baby, don't fall down on me now.
Just move it right here to the Harlem Shuffle. *(To Chorus:)*

Verse 3: (key of A minor)
Hitch, hitchhike, baby, across the floor.
Whoa, whoa, whoa, I can't stand it no more.

Now come on, baby, now get into your slide.
Just ride, ride, ride, little pony, ride.

Chorus:
Yeah, yeah, yeah, do the Harlem Shuffle.
Yeah, yeah, yeah, do the Harlem Shuffle. (Do the monkey shine.)
Yeah, yeah, yeah, shake a tail feather, baby.
Yeah, yeah, yeah, shake a tail feather, baby.
Yeah, yeah, yeah, do the Harlem Shuffle. *(Repeat and fade)*

I'D RATHER GO BLIND

Words and Music by
B. FOSTER and E. JORDAN

Some-thing told me ___ it was o - ver ___

When I saw you and him ___ talk - ing. ___

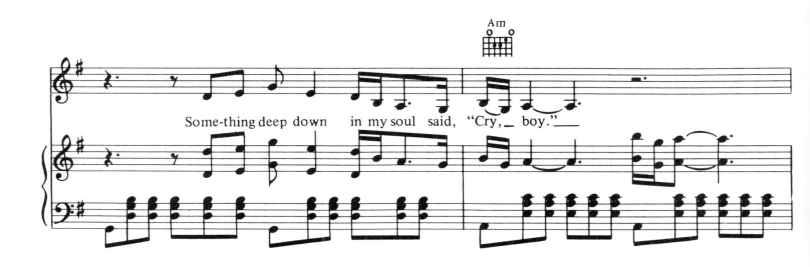

Some-thing deep down in my soul said, "Cry, ___ boy." ___

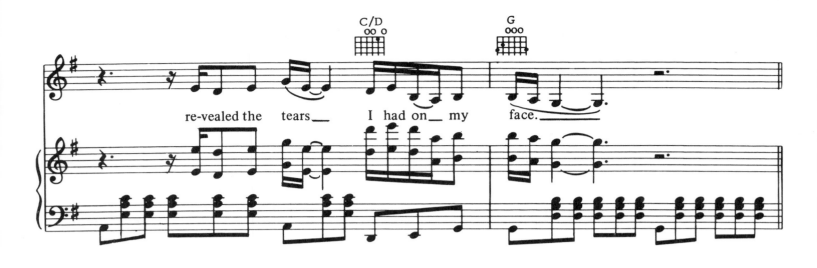

re-vealed the tears___ I had on___ my face.___

I would rath-er go___ blind, child.___

than to see you walk a - way___ from me.___

Repeat and fade

I'M GONNA TEAR YOUR PLAYHOUSE DOWN

Words and Music by
E. RANDLE

IN THE MIDNIGHT HOUR

Words by WILSON PICKETT
Music by STEVE CROPPER

IT'S IN HIS KISS

Words and Music by
RUDY CLARK

MANNISH BOY

Words and Music by
McKINLEY MORGANFIELD,
M. LONDON and E. McDANIEL

Now when I were a young boy . . .   at the age of five . . .

my mother said I'm gonna be . . .   the greatest man alive . . .

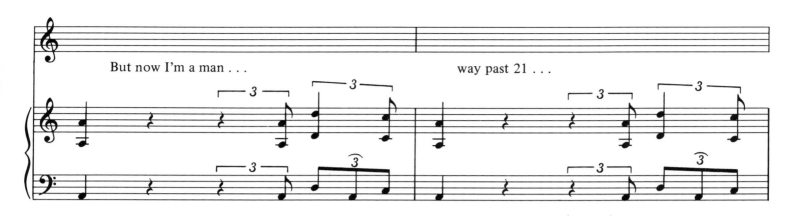

But now I'm a man . . .   way past 21 . . .

I'll never leave you baby . . .   I have lots of fun.. . .

SPOKEN BETWEEN RIFFS:

I'm a man . . .
I spell M . . .
H A . . .
N . . .
That represent me . . .
Muddy . . .
Oh child . . .
Why?
That means I'm a boy . . .
I'm a man . . .
I'm a full grown man . . .
I'm a man . . .
I'm a natural born lover's man . . .
I'm a man . . .
I'm a rolling stone . . .
I'm a man . . .
I'm a hootchie kootchie man . . .
Sitting on outside . . .
Just me and my mate . . .
You know I hate to move honey . . .
Come up two hours later . . .
When I'm a man . . .
I spell M . . .
H A . . .
N . . .
That represent me . . .
Muddy . . .
Oh child . . .
Why?
That mean mannish boy . . .

Man . . .
I'm a full grown man . . .
Man . . .
I'm a natural born lover's man . . .
Man . . .
I'm a rolling stone . . .
Man child . . .
I'm a hootchie kootchie man . . .
The lion I'll shoot . . .
And I'll never miss . . .
When I make love to a woman . . .
She can't resist . . .
I think I'll go down . . .
To old Kansas Dude . . .
And bring back my second cousin . . .
That little Johnny Cockaroo . . .
All you little girls . . .
Sitting out in line . . .
I could make love to you woman . . .
In five minutes' time . . .
Ain't that a man . . .
That mean mannish boy . . .
Man . . .
I'm a rolling stone . . .
I'm a man child . . .
I'm a hootchie kootchie man . . .
Well well well well . . .
Hey . . .
Here he is . . .
Ad lib. to Fade

NEED YOUR LOVE SO BAD

Words and Music by
LITTLE WILLIE JOHN

KNOCK ON WOOD

Words and Music by
EDDIE FLOYD and STEPHEN CROPPER

RESCUE ME

Words and Music by
CARL SMITH and RAYNARD MINER

VERSE 2:
Rescue me and take my heart
Take your love and comfort every part
'Cause I'm lonely and I'm blue
I need you and you're not true.

VERSE 3: — as Verse 1

VERSE 4:
Rescue me, come on and take my hand
Come on baby and be my man
'Cause I love you, 'cause I want you
Can't you see that I'm lonely.

RESPECT YOURSELF

Words and Music by
MACK RICE and LUTHER INGRAM

(1.) If you dis-re-spect ev-'ry-bo-dy that you run in-to,____ ah now what do you think a-ny-bo-dy's s'posed to re-spect you.____

1, 2.

2. If you
3.

VERSE 2:
If you don't give a heck
About the man with the Bible in his hand
Just get out the way
And let the gentleman do his thing.

VERSE 3:
You're the kind of gentleman
Who's got everything your way
Take the sheet off your face boy,
It's a brand new day.

VERSE 4:
If you're walking around thinking
That the world owes you something 'cause you're here
You're going out the world backwards
Like you did when you first come here.

VERSE 5:
Keep talking about the present
It won't stop evolution
Put your hand on your mouth
When you call, that'll help the solution.

VERSE 6:
Oh you're fussin' round womenfolk
And don't even know their name
Then you come and lock the fate
That'll make you a big hole there.

SHOUT

Words and Music by
O'KELLY ISLEY, RONALD ISLEY
and RUDOLPH ISLEY

VERSE 2:

Say!	Say!
Say that you love me	Come on now
Say!	Say!
Say that you need me	Come on now
Say!	Say!
Say that you want me	Come on now
Say!	Say!
You want to please me	Come on now.

VERSE 3:

You know you make me wanna shout,
Shout! . . .
Come on now . . .
Yeah yeah yeah . . .

SOUL MAN

Words and Music by
DAVID PORTER and ISAAC HAYES

give you hope___ and be your on-ly boy-friend. I'm a

soul man,___ I'm a soul man,___

I'm a

Verse 3

I was brought up on a side street,
I learned how to love before I could eat.
I was educated at Woodstock,
when I start lovin', oh, I just can't stop.

STAND BY ME

Words and Music by
BEN. E. KING, JERRY LEIBER and MIKE STOLLER

STORMY MONDAY

Words and Music by
T. BONE WALKER

and I tell you no-thing's oh so sad. _____

Faster, straight beat

VERSES 2 & 3:
The eagle flies on Friday
And Saturday I go out to play
The eagle flies on Friday
And Lord on Saturday I go out to play
And Sunday I go to church
And I just have to get on my knees and pray.

VERSE 4:
And I have to say Lord have mercy
Lord have mercy on me
Lord have mercy, have mercy
Lord have mercy on me.
I wanna see my baby yes I do
Lord send her home to me.

(TAKE A LITTLE) PIECE OF MY HEART

Words by BERT BURNS
Music by JERRY RAGOVOY

VERSE 2:
You're out on the street lookin' good
And you know deep down in your heart that ain't right.
And oh, you never never hear me when I cry at night
Woh, oh, I tell myself that I can't stand the pain
But when you hold me in your arms I say it again.

TAKE ME TO THE RIVER

Words and Music by
AL GREEN and MABAN LEWIS HODGES

(1.) I don't know why I love you like I do,___ af-ter all the chan-ges that

you put me through.___ Used all my mo-ney and my ci-gar-ettes,___

VERSE 2:

I don't know why she treated me so bad
After all the things that we could have had.
Love is a notion that I can't forget
My sweet sixteen I will never regret.

VERSE 3:

I don't know why I love you like I do
After all the things that you put me through.
There's sixteen candles burning on my wall
Tell me little baby, who's the fool of them all?

THINK

Words and Music by
ARETHA FRANKLIN
and TED WHITE